Summer Solutions.

Minutes a Day–Mastery for a Lifetime!

Standards-Based
Mathematics K

Nancy L. McGraw

Donna M. Mazzola

Nancy Tondy

Christopher Backs

Diane Dillon

Lori Lender

Simple Solutions Learning, Inc.

Beachwood, OH

Summer Solutions
Standards-Based Mathematics K

Printed in the United States of America

The writers of *Summer Solutions* Standards-Based Mathematics
aligned the series in accordance with information from the following:

National Governors Association Center for Best Practices,
Council of Chief State School Officers, Washington, D.C., 2010.

United States coin images from the United States Mint.

ISBN: 978-1-60873-508-2

Cover Design: Dan Mazzola
Editor: Randy Reetz

Instructions for Parents / Guardians

- *Summer Solutions* is an extension of the *Simple Solutions* approach being used by thousands of children in schools across the United States.

- This summer book aligns with specific standards that identify key ideas, understandings, and skills, and they emphasize a deep learning of math concepts appropriate for this particular grade level. The standards' codes are listed next to the reviewed skills.

- The 30 lessons included in each workbook are meant to review and reinforce the skills learned in the grade level just completed.

- The program is designed to be used three days per week for ten weeks to ensure retention.

- Completing the book all at one time defeats the purpose of sustained practice over the summer break.

- Each book contains answers for each lesson.

- Lessons should be checked immediately for optimal feedback. Items that were difficult for students or done incorrectly should be resolved to ensure mastery.

- Adjust the use of the book to fit vacations. More lessons may have to be completed during the weeks before or following a family vacation.

Summer Solutions
Standards-Based Mathematics K

Reviewed Skills Include	Standard
• Count to 100 by Ones and Tens	K.CC.1
• Count to Answer "How Many?"	K.CC.5
• Correctly Name Shapes Regardless of Orientation or Size	K.G.2
• Model Shapes in the World by Building or Drawing Shapes	K.G.5
• Directly Compare Two Objects to see Which Has More or Less of an Attribute	K.MD.2
• Count Forward from Any Given Number 1 – 99	K.CC.2
• Compare Two Groups to Determine Greater Than, Less Than, or Equal To	K.CC.6
• Represent Addition and Subtraction with Objects, Drawings, or Equations	K.OA.1
• Identify Shapes as Two- or Three-Dimensional	K.G.3
• Analyze and Compare Two- and Three-Dimensional Shapes by Attributes	K.G.4
• Decompose Numbers Less than or Equal to 10 in Various Ways	K.OA.3
• Compare Two Numbers between 1 and 10 Presented as Written Numerals	K.CC.7
• Classify Objects into Given Categories / Sort Categories by Count	K.MD.3
• Solve Addition and Subtraction Word Problems Within 10	K.OA.2
• For Any Number 1 – 9, Find the Number that Makes 10	K.OA.4
• Compose Simple Shapes to Form Larger Shapes	K.G.6
• Compose and Decompose Numbers from 11 – 19 into Ten Ones and Further Ones	K.NBT.1
• Fluently Add and Subtract Within 5	K.OA.5

Lesson #1

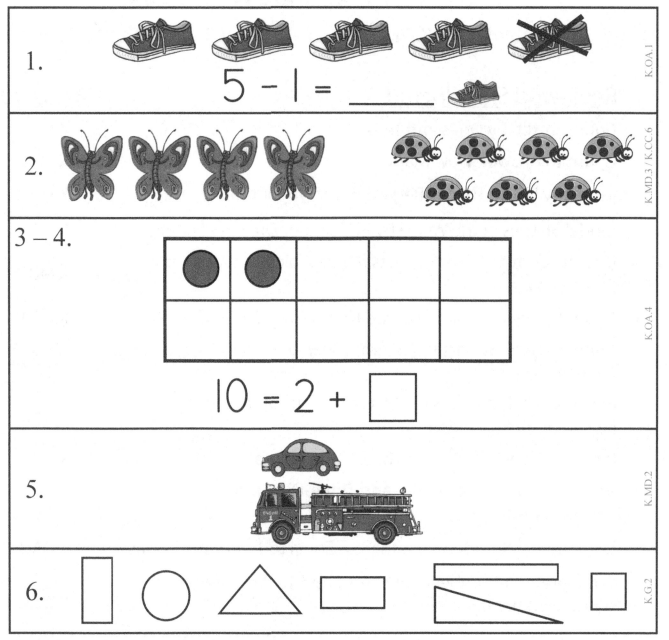

Directions:

1. There are 5 shoes, and 1 shoe is taken away. How many shoes are left?
    Write the difference on the line.

2. Count the objects in each group. Circle the group that has 7.

3 – 4.   Draw the missing circles to make ten. Write the number of circles you drew in the
          box to complete the equation.

5. Circle the vehicle that is **longer**.

6. Color the rectangles.

Lesson #2

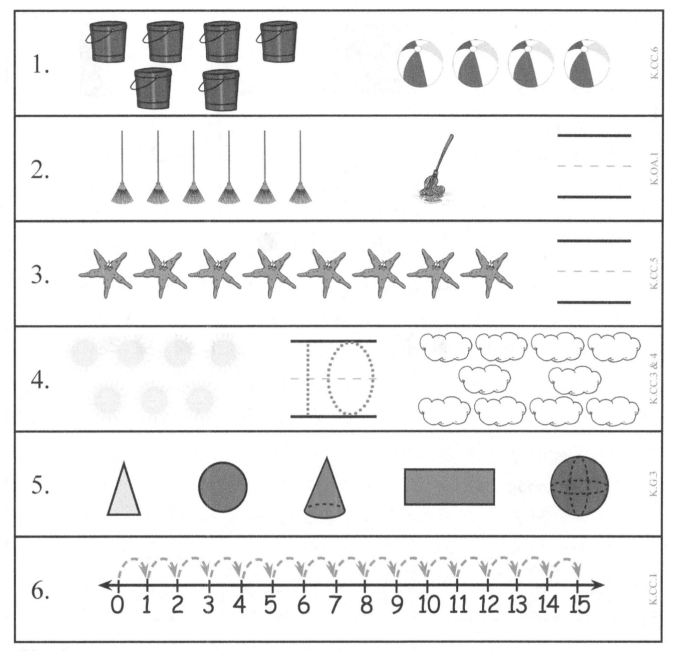

Directions:

1. Count the objects in each group. Which group is **less than** the other? Circle it.

2. Jim's dad has 6 rakes and 1 mop in the garage. How many tools are there in Jim's garage in all? Write the number on the line.

3. Count the starfish. How many are there? Write the number.

4. Trace the number 10. Count the objects in each group. Circle the group that has 10.

5. Circle the **three-dimensional** shapes.

6. Trace the lines as you count up to 15.

Lesson #3

1. K.G.6

2. $4 - 0 = \underline{\hphantom{00}}$ $3 - 3 = \underline{\hphantom{00}}$

$2 - 1 = \underline{\hphantom{00}}$ $4 - 2 = \underline{\hphantom{00}}$ K.OA.5

3 – 4.

$4 = \underline{\hphantom{00}} + \underline{\hphantom{00}}$

$4 = \underline{\hphantom{00}} + \underline{\hphantom{00}}$ $4 = \underline{\hphantom{00}} + \underline{\hphantom{00}}$ K.OA.3

5.   hexagon   K.G.5

6. 43 __ 45 46 __ __   K.CC.2

Directions:

1.   Trace the dotted lines. What shape can be made from 4 squares? Circle the shape.

2.   Write the differences.

3 – 4.   There are different ways to make a sum of 4. Finish the number sentences.

5.   Complete the hexagons by tracing the lines. Then, draw your own hexagon.

6.   Write the missing numbers.

Lesson #4

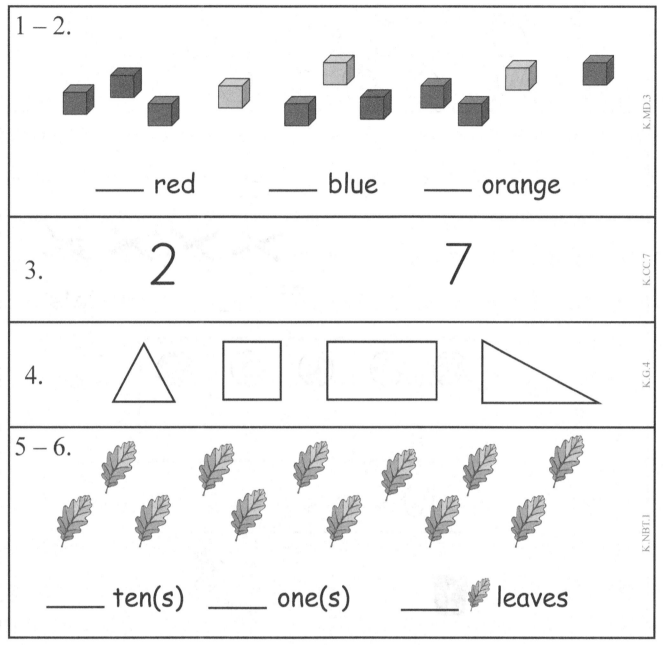

Directions:

1 – 2.   Sort the objects by color. How many are red? How many are blue? How many are orange? Circle the color word for the group that has **the most**.

3.   Circle the number that is **less**.

4.   Color the shapes that have 3 corners.

5 – 6.   Circle the groups of ten. Write how many tens and ones. How many leaves are there in all?

Lesson #5

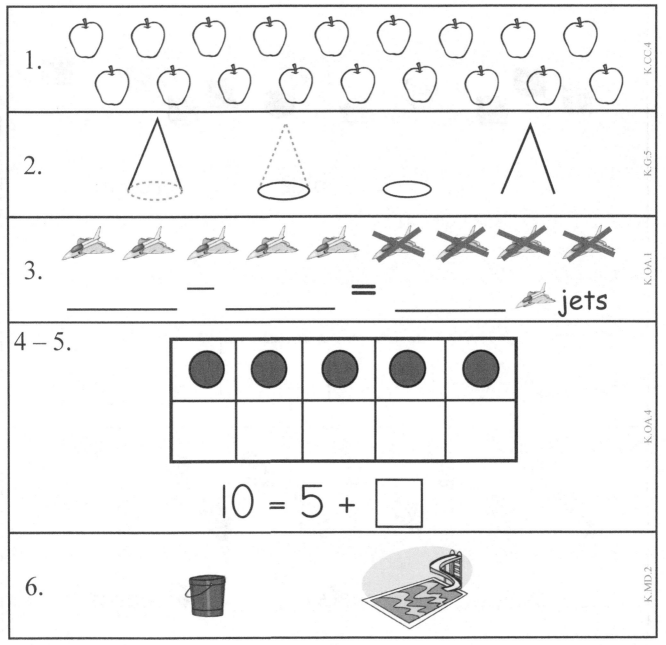

Directions:

1.   Color in 14 apples.

2.   Trace the lines to complete the first two cones. Draw the missing parts of the last two cones.

3.   Jeff saw 9 jets in the sky. Then, 4 of the jets flew away. How many jets were left? Fill in the number sentence.

4 – 5.   Draw the missing circles to make ten. Write the number of circles you drew in the box to complete the equation.

6.   Circle the object that holds **less**.

Lesson #6

1.
$$2 + 0 = \underline{\hspace{1cm}}$$
$$0 + 5 = \underline{\hspace{1cm}}$$
$$3 + 1 = \underline{\hspace{1cm}}$$
$$2 + 2 = \underline{\hspace{1cm}}$$

K.OA.5

2.

K.G.3

3.

$$1O \quad 11$$

K.CC.5

4.

$$\underline{\hspace{2cm}} + \underline{\hspace{2cm}} = \underline{\hspace{2cm}}$$

K.OA.1

5.

K.G.2

6.

K.CC.6

Directions:

1. Write the sums.

2. Color the **two-dimensional** shapes.

3. Count the flags. How many are there? Circle the number.

4. There are 6 rings. One more ring is added. How many rings are there in all?
Fill in the number sentence.

5. Circle the triangles.

6. Count the objects in each group. Which group is **greater than** the other? Circle it.

Lesson #7

1 – 2.

7 = _____ + _____   7 = _____ + _____

7 = _____ + _____   7 = _____ + _____

3. rectangles

4.

$$15 = 10 + \text{\_\_\_}$$

5.

6.

Directions:

1 – 2.   There are many ways to make a sum of 7. Finish the number sentences.

3.   Draw 3 rectangles.

4.   The number 15 has 1 group of ten and 5 ones, so 15 = 10 + 5. Finish the number sentence.

5.   Trace the dotted lines. What shape can be made from 4 triangles? Circle the shape.

6.   Trace the number 6. Count the objects in each group. Circle the group that has 6.

Lesson #8

1.   6   6 | K.CC.7

2. $1 + 4 =$ ____ $5 + 0 =$ ____

      $3 - 2 =$ ____ $0 - 0 =$ ____   K.OA.5

3.   K.G.4

4.   K.OA.1

      ____ + ____ = ____

5 – 6.   K.CC.1

      10 ____   30 40 50 ____ ____ 80

Directions:

1. Circle the numbers that are **equal**.

2. Write the sums and differences.

3. Circle the shapes that have corners.

4. Mrs. Lee handed out 5 bottles of glue and 5 pairs of scissors to her art students. How many art supplies did Mrs. Lee hand out in all? Fill in the number sentence.

5 – 6.   Count by 10s and fill in the missing numbers.

Lesson #9

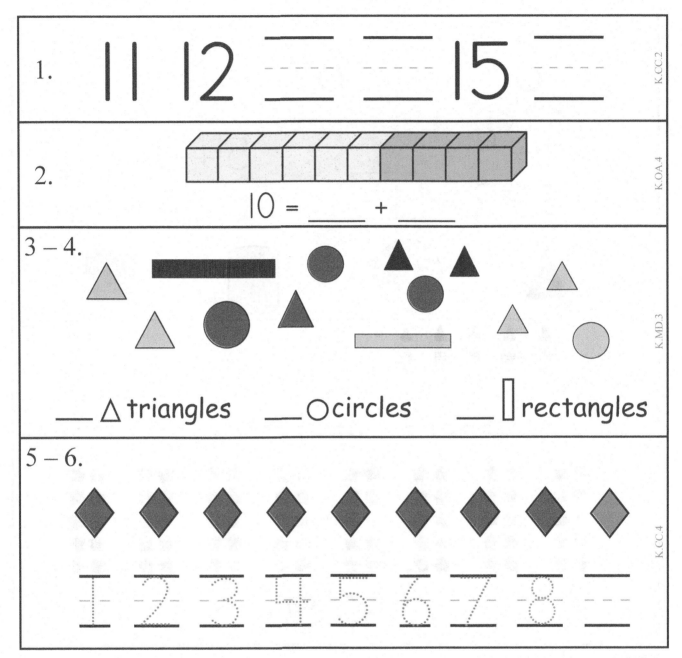

1. 11 12 __ __ 15 __

2. $10 = \underline{\quad} + \underline{\quad}$

3 – 4.

__△ triangles   __○ circles   __▯ rectangles

5 – 6.

1 2 3 4 5 6 7 8

Directions:

1.   Write the missing numbers.

2.   There are 10 cubes. How many cubes are yellow? How many cubes are green? Finish the equation.

3 – 4.   Sort the objects by shape. How many are triangles? How many are circles? How many are rectangles? Circle the shape for the group that has the **fewest**.

5 – 6.   There are eight red diamonds. One more blue diamond has been added. Count the diamonds. As you count, write the number under each diamond.

Lesson #10

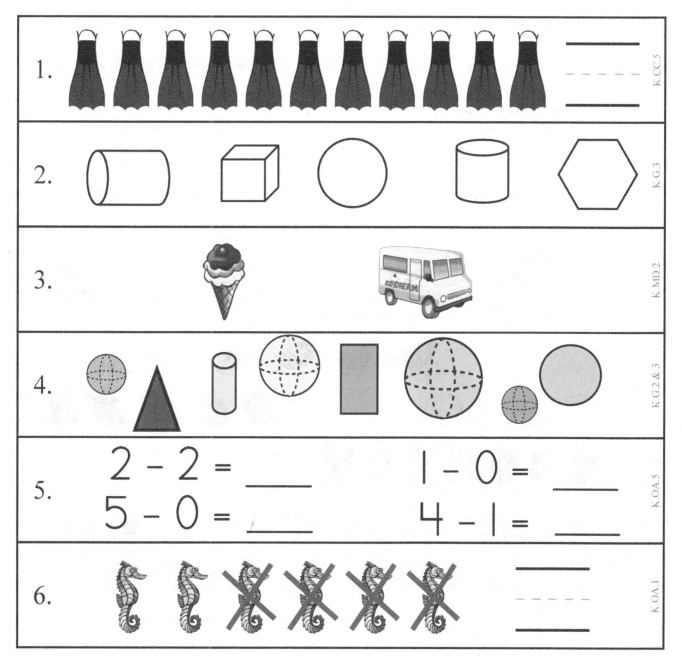

Directions:

1. Count the flippers. How many are there? Write the number.

2. Color the **three-dimensional** shapes.

3. Circle the object that is **heavier**.

4. Circle the spheres.

5. Write the differences.

6. There are 6 seahorses. Then 4 seahorses swim away. How many seahorses are left? Write the number on the line.

Lesson #11

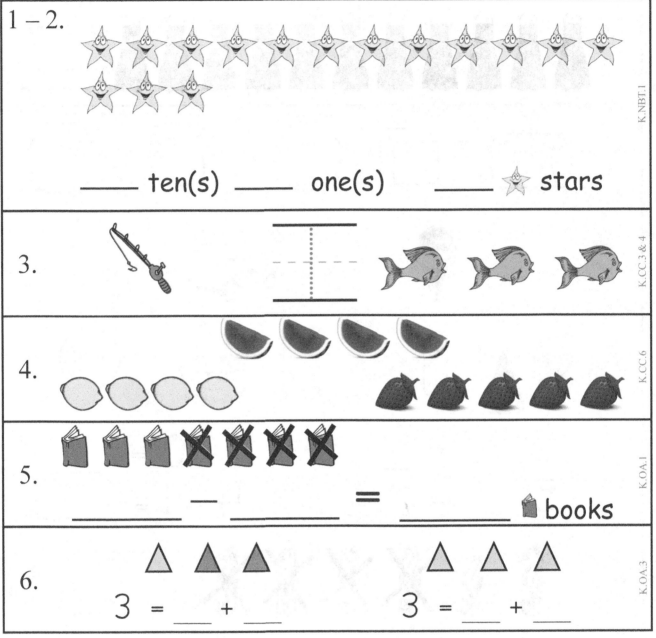

1 – 2.

_____ ten(s) _____ one(s)   _____ ⭐ stars

K.NBT.1

3.

K.CC.3 & 4

4.

K.CC.6

5.

_____ __ _____ = _____ 📘 books

K.OA.1

6.

3 = ___ + ___   3 = ___ + ___

K.OA.3

Directions:

1 – 2.   Circle the groups of ten. Write how many tens and ones. How many stars are there in all?

3.   Trace the number 1. Count the objects in each group. Circle the group that has 1.

4.   Count the watermelons. Which group is **equal to** the watermelons? Circle it.

5.   Sarah borrowed 7 books from the library on Monday. She returned 4 of the books on Friday. How many books were left? Fill in the number sentence.

6.   There are different ways to make a sum of 3. Finish the number sentences.

Lesson #12

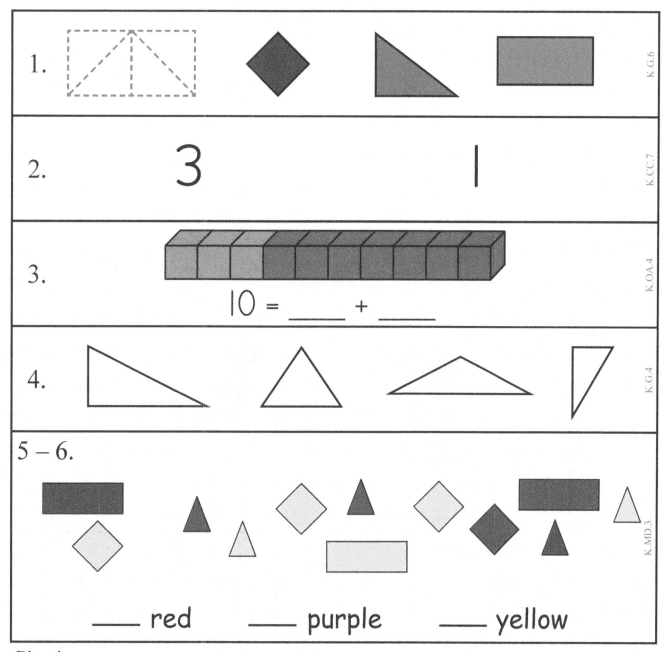

Directions:

1.   Trace the dotted lines. What shape can be made from 4 triangles? Circle the shape.

2.   Circle the number that is **greater**.

3.   There are 10 cubes. How many cubes are orange? How many cubes are red? Finish
     the equation.

4.   Color the triangle that has 3 sides of equal length.

5 – 6.   Sort the objects by color. How many are red? How many are purple? How many
         are yellow? Circle the color word for the group that has **the most**.

Lesson #13

1. 10 20 ___ 40 50 60 ___ 80 90 ___   K.CC.1

2. _____ + _____ = _____   K.OA.1

3.
$1 + 1 =$ ___ $2 + 3 =$ ___

$0 + 2 =$ ___ $1 + 0 =$ ___   K.OA.5

4.   K.MD.2

5.   K.G.5

6. 88 ___ ___ 91 ___ 93   K.CC.2

Directions:

1. Count by 10s and fill in the missing numbers.

2. There are 4 cupcakes. One more cupcake is added. How many cupcakes are there in all? Fill in the number sentence.

3. Write the sums.

4. Circle the object that is **lighter**.

5. Trace the lines to complete the cylinders. Then draw 2 more cylinders.

6. Write the missing numbers.

Lesson #14

1.

2. 1 8 20

3 – 4.

$8 = \underline{\quad} + \underline{\quad}$ $8 = \underline{\quad} + \underline{\quad}$

$8 = \underline{\quad} + \underline{\quad}$ $8 = \underline{\quad} + \underline{\quad}$

5.

6.

Directions:

1. Circle the **two-dimensional** shapes.

2. Count the baseballs. How many are there? Circle the number.

3 – 4. There are many ways to make a sum of 8. Finish the number sentences.

5. Count the objects in each group. Which group is **less than** the other? Circle it.

6. Color the squares.

Lesson #15

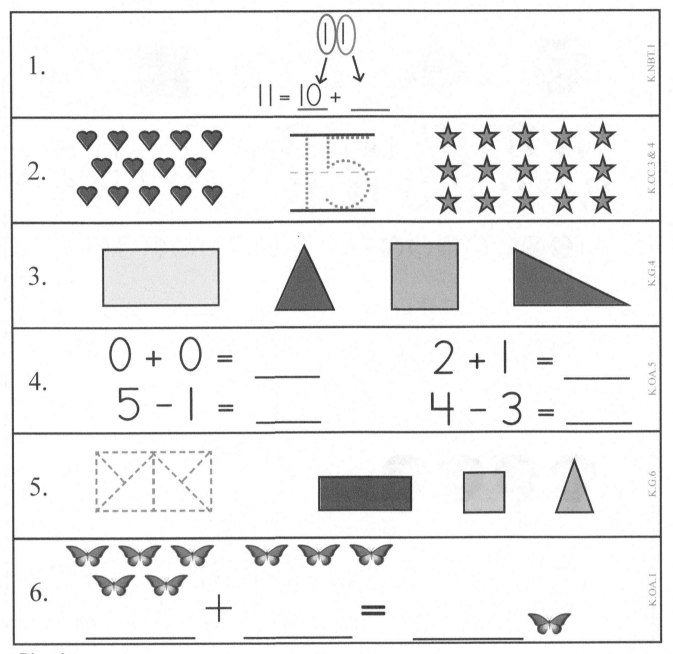

Directions:

1. The number 11 has 1 group of ten and 1 one, so 11 = 10 + 1. Finish the number sentence.

2. Trace the number 15. Count the objects in each group. Circle the group that has 15.

3. Circle the shapes that have 4 corners.

4. Write the sums and differences.

5. Trace the dotted lines. What shape can be made from 6 triangles? Circle the shape.

6. Peter saw 5 butterflies in the garden. Three more butterflies flew into the garden. How many butterflies were in the garden in all? Fill in the number sentence.

Lesson #16

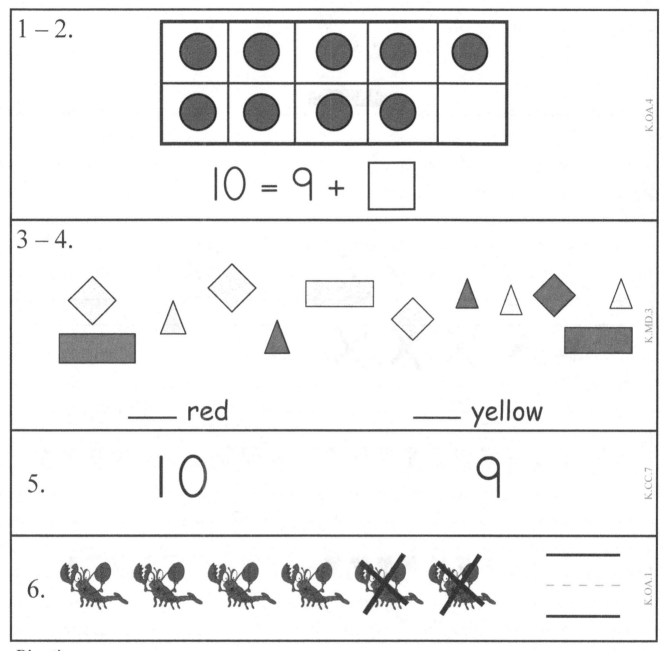

1 – 2.

10 = 9 + ☐

K.OA.4

3 – 4.

____ red   ____ yellow

K.MD.3

5.   10   9

K.CC.7

6.

— — — — —
_____

K.OA.1

Directions:

1 – 2.   Draw the missing circles to make ten. Write the number of circles you drew in the box to complete the equation.

3 – 4.   Sort the objects by color. How many are red? How many are yellow? Circle the color word for the group that has **fewer**.

5.   Circle the number that is **less**.

6.   There are 6 lobsters. Then 2 of the lobsters walk away. How many lobsters are left? Write the number on the line.

Lesson #17

1.

                                           K.MD.2

2. triangle △

                                           K.G.5

3. 20 ___ 22 ___ 24 ___

                                           K.CC.2

4.

      _____ − _____ = _____ birds

                                           K.OA.2

5 – 6. ♡♡♡♡♡♡♡♡♡♡   ♡♡♡♡♡♡♡♡♡♡

     10 = ___ + ___   10 = ___ + ___

     ♡♡♡♡♡♡♡♡♡♡   ♡♡♡♡♡♡♡♡♡♡

     10 = ___ + ___   10 = ___ + ___

                                           K.OA.3

Directions:

1.   Circle the child that is **shorter**.

2.   Trace the triangle. Draw 3 more triangles.

3.   Write the missing numbers.

4.   There were 5 birds in the tree. Then 3 birds flew away. How many birds were left in the tree? Fill in the number sentence.

5 – 6.   There are many ways to make a sum of 10. Finish the number sentences.

Lesson #18

1. $5 - 2 =$ ___ $3 - 1 =$ ___
    $3 - 0 =$ ___ $5 - 5 =$ ___
K.OA.5

2.
K.G.3

3. 40 ___ 60 ___ 80 ___ 100
K.CC.1

4.

    $2 + 1 =$ ___
K.OA.1

5.   ___
                                                                          ___
K.CC.5

6.
K.G.6

Directions:

1. Write the differences.

2. Circle the **three-dimensional** shapes.

3. Count by 10s and fill in the missing numbers.

4. There are 2 pies. One more pie is added. How many pies are there in all? Finish the number sentence.

5. Count the scooters. How many are there? Write the number.

6. Trace the dotted lines. What shape can be made from a square and 4 triangles? Circle the shape.

Lesson #19

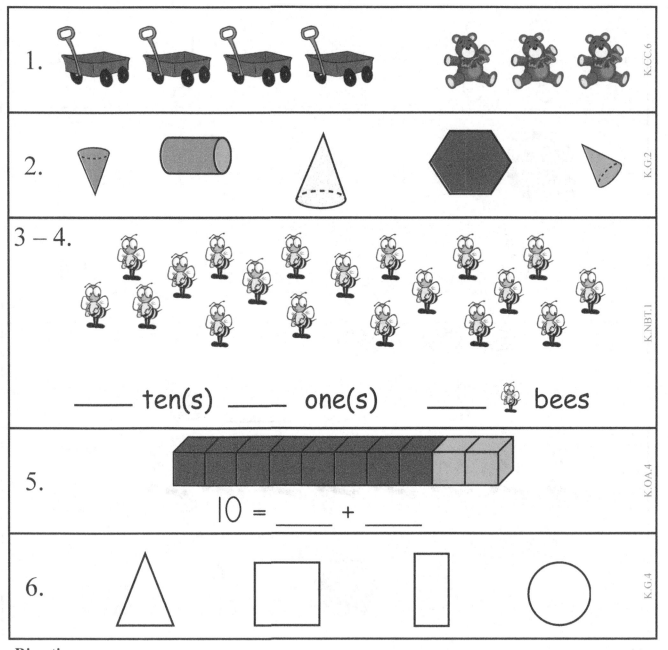

1.

2.

3 – 4.

_____ ten(s) _____ one(s)   _____ bees

5. $10 = \underline{\quad} + \underline{\quad}$

6.

Directions:

1.   Count the objects in each group. Which group is **greater than** the other? Circle it.

2.   Circle the cones.

3 – 4.   Circle a group of ten. Write how many tens and ones. How many bees are there in all?

5.   There are 10 cubes. How many cubes are purple? How many cubes are green? Finish the equation.

6.   Color the shapes that have 4 sides.

Lesson #20

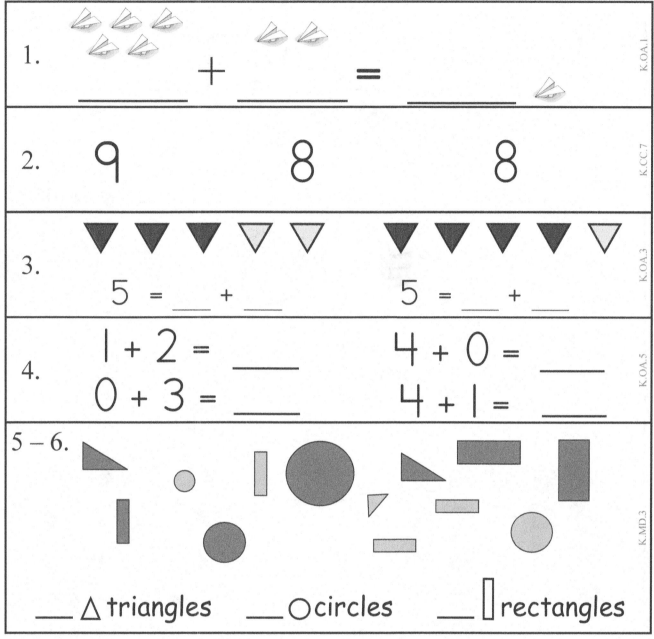

1. _____ + _____ = _____

2. 9   8   8

3. 5 = ___ + ___   5 = ___ + ___

4.
$$1 + 2 = \underline{\quad}$$
$$0 + 3 = \underline{\quad}$$
$$4 + 0 = \underline{\quad}$$
$$4 + 1 = \underline{\quad}$$

5 – 6.

___ △ triangles   ___ ○ circles   ___ ▯ rectangles

Directions:

1. Jamal made 5 paper airplanes. Simon made 2 paper airplanes. How many paper airplanes are there in all? Fill in the number sentence.

2. Circle the numbers that are **equal**.

3. There are different ways to make a sum of 5. Finish the number sentences.

4. Write the sums.

5 – 6. Sort the objects by shape. How many are triangles? How many are circles? How many are rectangles? Circle the shape for the group that has the **most**.

Lesson #21

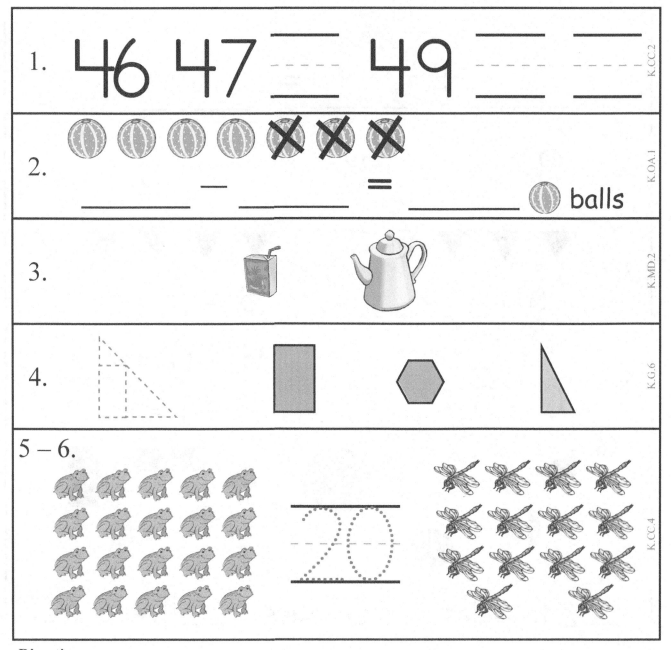

Directions:

1.   Write the missing numbers.

2.   There are 7 balls. Three balls are taken away. How many balls are left? Fill in the number sentence.

3.   Circle the object that holds **more**.

4.   Trace the dotted lines. What shape can be made from a rectangle and 2 triangles? Circle the shape.

5 – 6.   Trace the number 20. Count the objects in each group. Circle the group that has 20.

Lesson #22

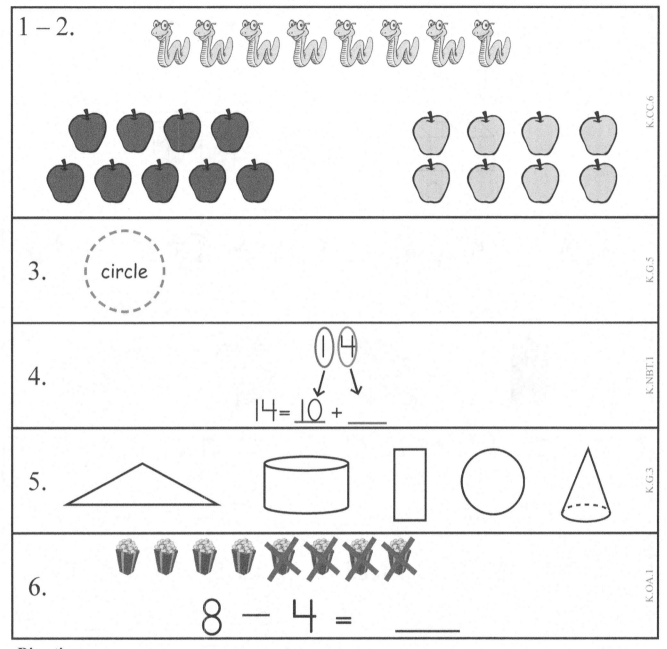

Directions:

1 – 2.   Count the worms. Which group is **equal to** the worms? Circle it.

3.   Trace the circle. Draw 3 more circles.

4.   The number 14 has 1 group of ten and 4 ones, so 14 = 10 + 4. Finish the number sentence.

5.   Color the **two-dimensional** shapes.

6.   Jack got 8 presents for his birthday. He opened 4 of the presents. How many presents did Jack have left to open? Finish the number sentence.

Lesson #23

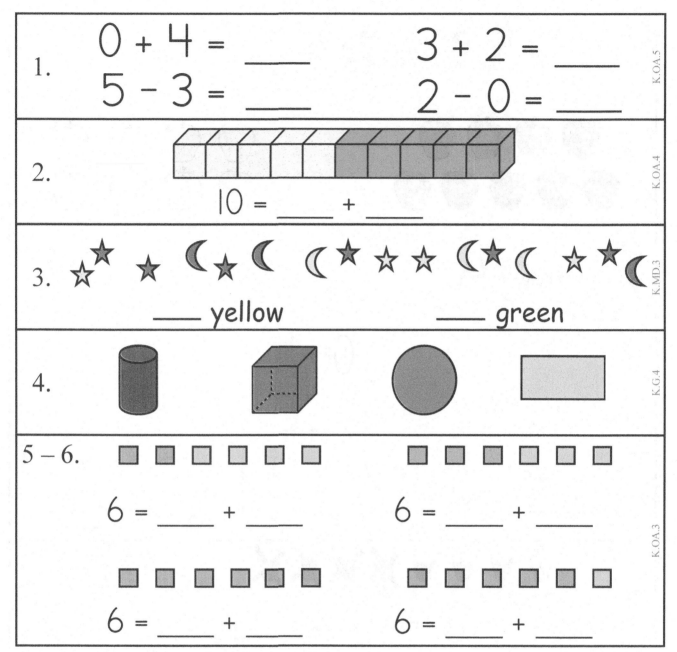

1. $0 + 4 =$ ___ $3 + 2 =$ ___
   $5 - 3 =$ ___ $2 - 0 =$ ___

   K.OA.5

2. $10 =$ ___ $+$ ___

   K.OA.4

3. ___ yellow   ___ green

   K.MD.3

4.

   K.G.4

5 – 6.

   $6 =$ ___ $+$ ___ $6 =$ ___ $+$ ___

   $6 =$ ___ $+$ ___ $6 =$ ___ $+$ ___

   K.OA.3

Directions:

1. Write the sums and differences.

2. There are 10 cubes. How many cubes are yellow? How many cubes are orange? Finish the equation.

3. Sort the objects by color. How many are yellow? How many are green? Circle the color word for the group that has **more**.

4. Circle the shapes that do **not** have corners.

5 – 6.   There are different ways to make a sum of 6. Finish the number sentences.

Lesson #24

1.

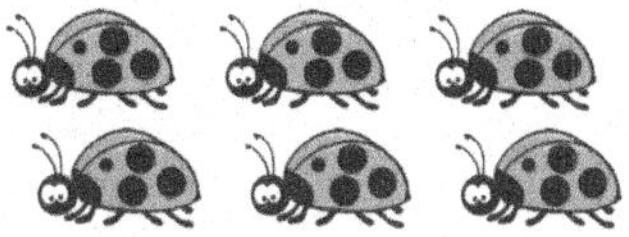

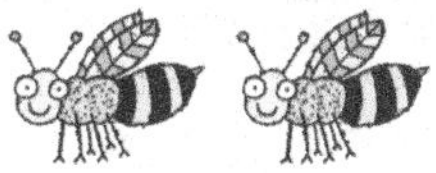

___ + ___ = ___ insects

K.OA.1

2.

9 5

K.CC.5

3.

K.G.2

4. 2 0

K.CC.7

5.

K.MD.2

6. 10 20 ___ ___ 50 ___ ___

K.CC.1 & 2

Directions:

1. There are 6 ladybugs and 2 bees. How many insects are there in all? Fill in the number sentence.
2. Count the sandcastles. How many are there? Circle the number.
3. Color the cubes.
4. Circle the number that is **greater**.
5. Circle the object that is **heavier**.
6. Count by 10s and fill in the missing numbers.

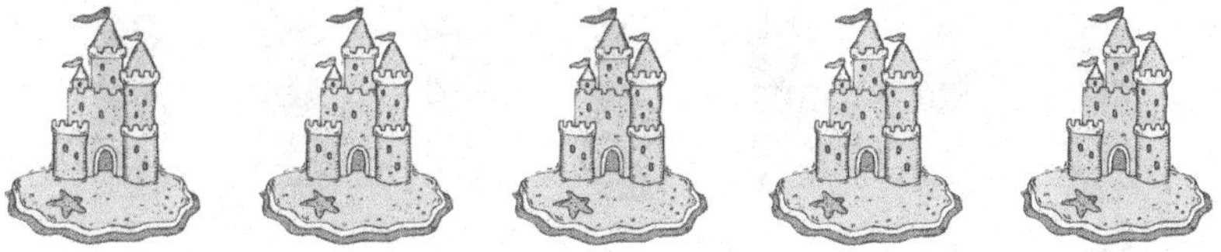

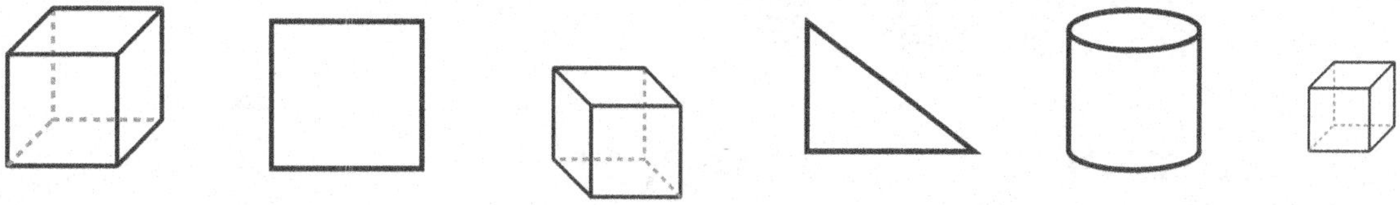

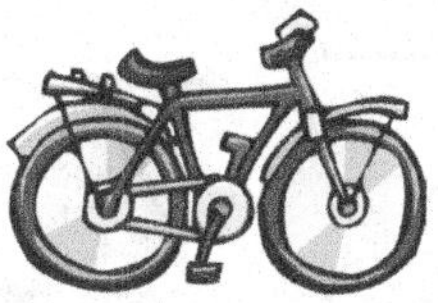

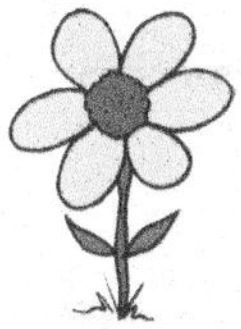

Lesson #25

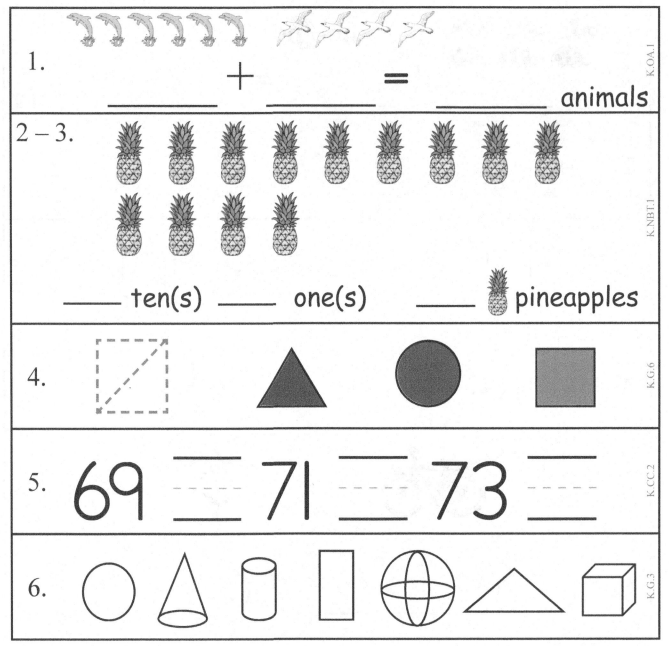

1. _____ + _____ = _____ animals

2 – 3. _____ ten(s) _____ one(s) _____ pineapples

4.

5. 69 ___ ___ 71 ___ ___ 73 ___ ___

6.

Directions:

1. At the beach, Julia saw 6 dolphins swimming in the ocean. She also saw 4 seagulls flying over the ocean. How many animals did Julia see in all? Fill in the sentence.

2 – 3. Circle the groups of ten. Write how many tens and ones. How many pineapples are there in all?

4. Trace the dotted lines. What shape can be made from 2 triangles? Circle the shape.

5. Write the missing numbers.

6. Color the **three-dimensional** shapes.

Lesson #26

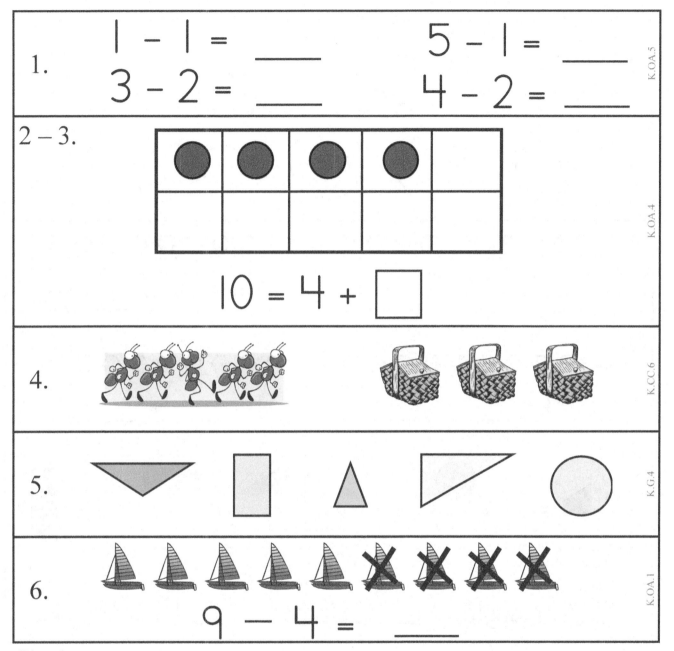

1.

$$1 - 1 = \underline{\quad}$$
$$3 - 2 = \underline{\quad}$$
$$5 - 1 = \underline{\quad}$$
$$4 - 2 = \underline{\quad}$$

K.OA.5

2 – 3.

$$10 = 4 + \square$$

K.OA.4

4.

K.CC.6

5.

K.G.4

6.

$$9 - 4 = \underline{\quad}$$

K.OA.1

Directions:

1.   Write the differences.

2 – 3.   Draw the missing circles to make ten. Write the number of circles you drew in the box to complete the equation.

4.   Count the objects in each group. Which group is **less than** the other? Circle it.

5.   Circle the shapes that have 3 sides.

6.   There are 9 boats. Then 4 boats sail away. How many boats are left? Finish the number sentence.

Lesson #27

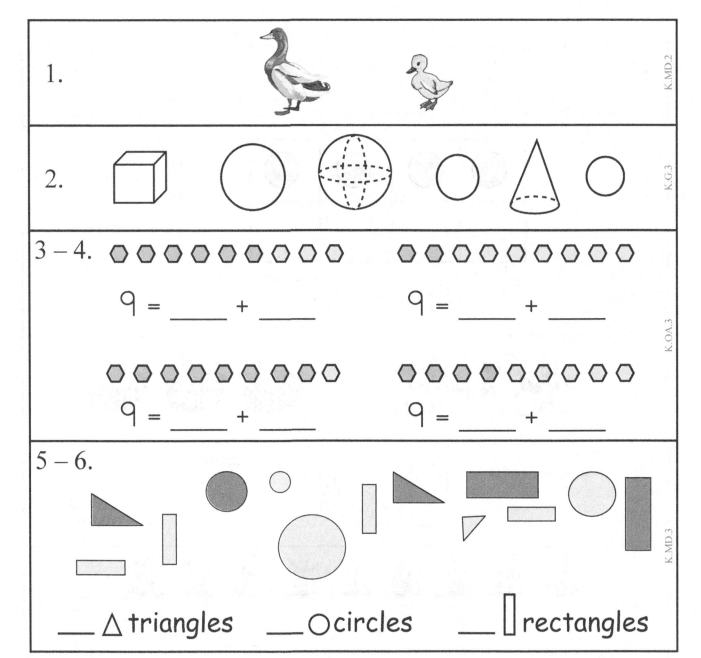

1.

2.

3 – 4.

$9 = \underline{\hspace{1cm}} + \underline{\hspace{1cm}}$

$9 = \underline{\hspace{1cm}} + \underline{\hspace{1cm}}$

$9 = \underline{\hspace{1cm}} + \underline{\hspace{1cm}}$

$9 = \underline{\hspace{1cm}} + \underline{\hspace{1cm}}$

5 – 6.

__△ triangles   __○ circles   __▯ rectangles

K.MD.2

K.G.3

K.OA.3

K.MD.3

Directions:

1. Circle the duck that is **taller**.

2. Color the **two-dimensional** shapes.

3 – 4. There are many ways to make a sum of 9. Finish the number sentences.

5 – 6. Sort the objects by shape. How many are triangles? How many are circles?
How many are rectangles? Circle the shape for the group that has the **fewest**.

Lesson #28

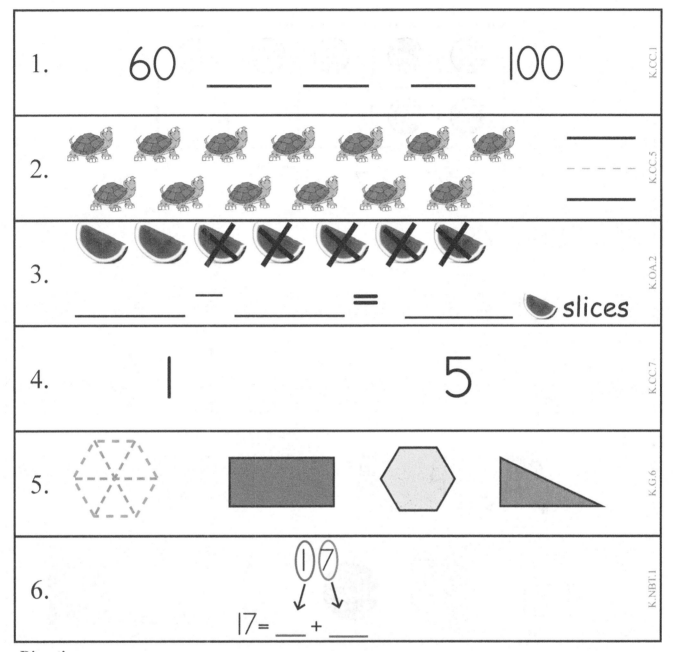

Directions:

1. Count by 10s and fill in the missing numbers.

2. Count the turtles. How many are there? Write the number.

3. Frank brought 7 slices of watermelon to the picnic. If 5 slices of watermelon had been eaten, how many slices of watermelon were left? Fill in the number sentence.

4. Circle the number that is **less**.

5. Trace the dotted lines. What shape can be made from 6 triangles? Circle the shape.

6. The number 17 has 1 group of ten and 7 ones, so $17 = 10 + 7$. Finish the number sentence.

Lesson #29

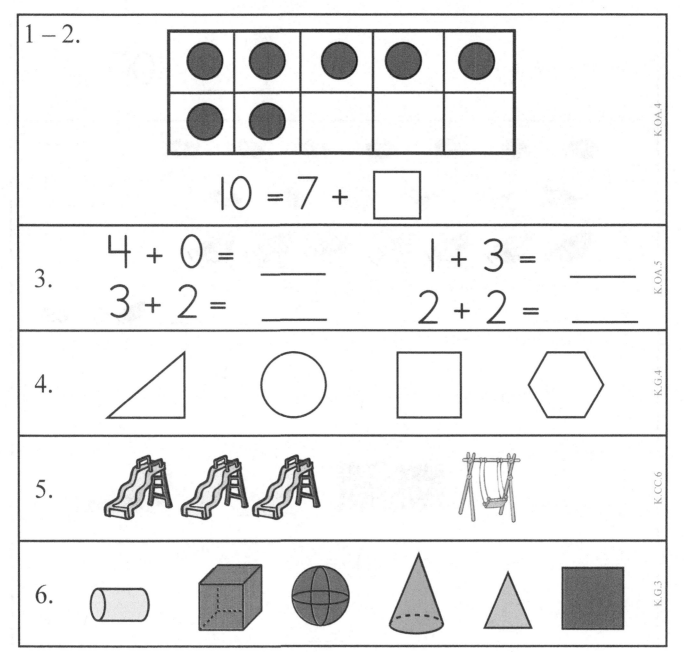

Directions:

1 – 2. Draw the missing circles to make ten. Write the number of circles you drew in the box to complete the equation.

3. Write the sums.

4. Color the shapes that have sides.

5. Count the objects in each group. Which group is **greater than** the other? Circle it.

6. Circle the **two-dimensional** shapes.

Lesson #30

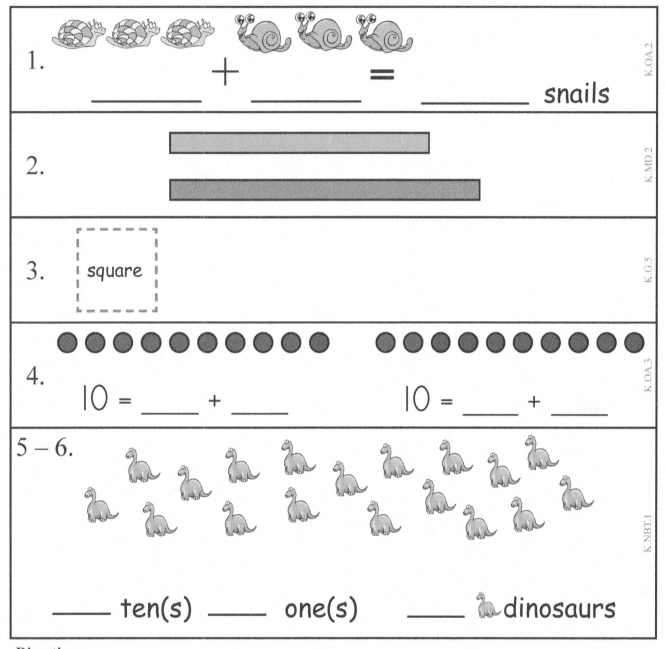

1.

_____ + _____ = _____ snails

2.

3.   square

4. $10 = \text{\_\_\_\_} + \text{\_\_\_\_}$ $10 = \text{\_\_\_\_} + \text{\_\_\_\_}$

5 – 6.

____ ten(s) ____ one(s)   ____ dinosaurs

Directions:

1.   There are 3 snails. Three more snails crawl over to join them. How many snails are there all together? Fill in the number sentence.

2.   Circle the rectangle that is **shorter**.

3.   Trace the square. Draw 3 more squares.

4.   There are many ways to make a sum of 10. Finish the number sentences.

5 – 6.   Circle the groups of ten. Write how many tens and ones. How many dinosaurs are there in all?

Standards-Based Mathematics **K**

Answers to Lessons

Lesson #1	Lesson #2
1. $5 - 1 = \underline{4}$	**1.**
2.	**2.** 7
3 – 4. $10 = 2 + \boxed{8}$	**3.** 8
	4. 10
5.	**5.**
6.	**6.**

Lesson #3	Lesson #4
1.	1 – 2.
2. $4 - 0 = \underline{4}$ $3 - 3 = \underline{0}$ $2 - 1 = \underline{1}$ $4 - 2 = \underline{2}$	$\underline{2}$ red $\underline{6}$ blue $\underline{3}$ orange
3 – 4. $4 = \underline{3} + \underline{1}$ $4 = \underline{2} + \underline{2}$ $4 = \underline{1} + \underline{3}$	3. ②
	4.
5.	5 – 6. $\underline{1}$ ten(s) $\underline{2}$ one(s) $\underline{12}$ leaves
6. $43\ \cancel{44}\ 45\ 46\ \cancel{47}\ \cancel{48}$	

Lesson #5	Lesson #6
1. 	1. $2 + 0 = \underline{2}$ $3 + 1 = \underline{4}$ $0 + 5 = \underline{5}$ $2 + 2 = \underline{4}$
2. 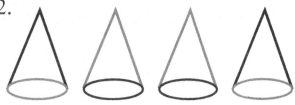	2. 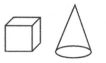
3. 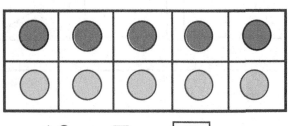 $\underline{9} - \underline{4} = \underline{5}$ jets	3. 
4 – 5.	4. $\underline{6} + \underline{1} = \underline{7}$
$10 = 5 + \boxed{5}$	5. 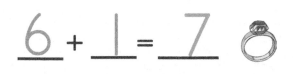 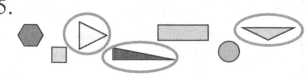
6. 	6. 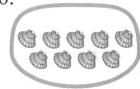 

Lesson #7	Lesson #8

Lesson #7

1 – 2.

$7 = \underline{3} + \underline{4}$ $7 = \underline{5} + \underline{2}$

$7 = \underline{1} + \underline{6}$ $7 = \underline{7} + \underline{0}$

3.

4.

$15 = \underline{10} + \underline{5}$

5.

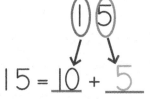

6.

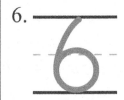 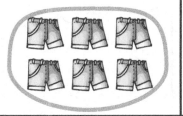

Lesson #8

1.

2.

$1 + 4 = \underline{5}$ $5 + 0 = \underline{5}$

$3 - 2 = \underline{1}$ $0 - 0 = \underline{0}$

3.

 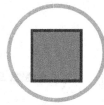

4.

$\underline{5} + \underline{5} = \underline{10}$

5 – 6.

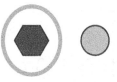

10   $\underline{20}$ 30   40   50 $\underline{60}$ $\underline{70}$ 80

Lesson #9	**Lesson #10**
1. 11 12 13 14 15 16	1. II
2. 10 = _6_ + _4_	2.
3 – 4. _7_ △ triangles _4_ ○ circles _2_ 0 rectangles	3.
	4.
5 – 6. 1 2 3 4 5 6 7 8 9	5. 2 - 2 = _0_ 1 - 0 = _1_ 5 - 0 = _5_ 4 - 1 = _3_
	6. 2

Lesson #11	Lesson #12

Lesson #11

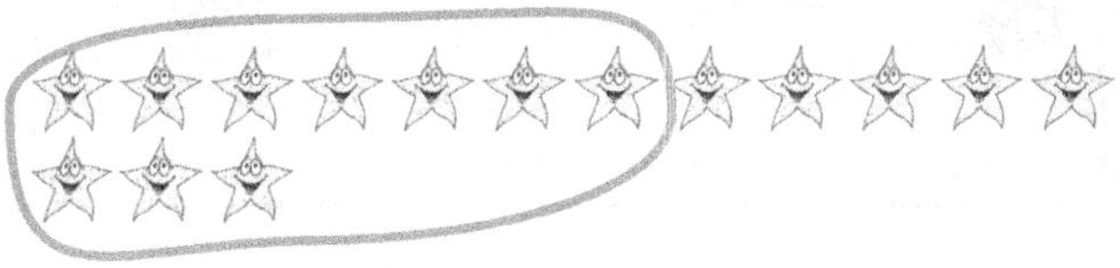

1 – 2.

_1_ ten(s) _5_ one(s)   _15_ ⭐ stars

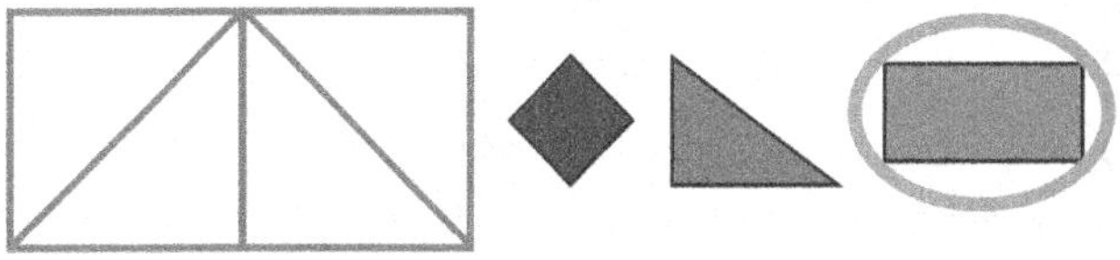

3.

4.

5.

$7 - 4 = 3$ 📕 books

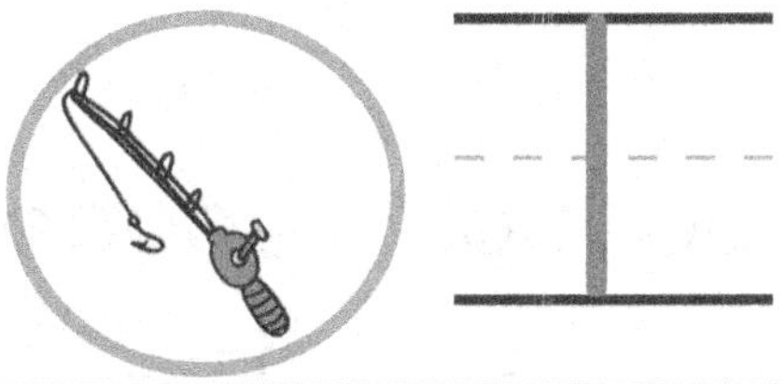

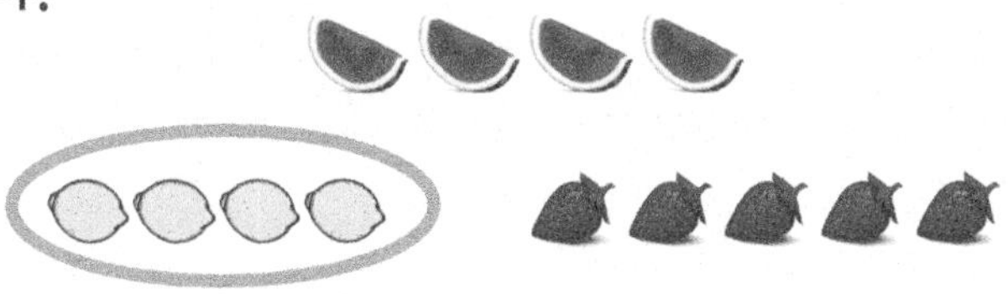

6.

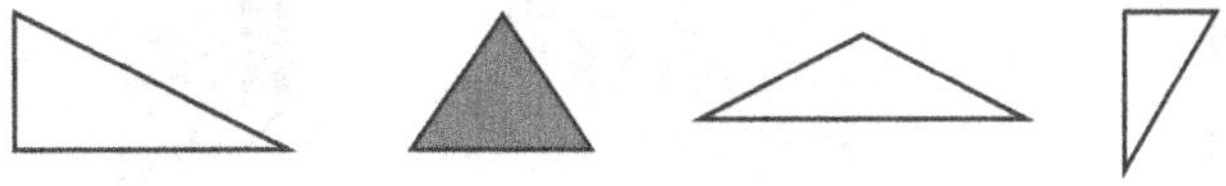

$3 = \underline{1} + \underline{2}$ $3 = \underline{3} + \underline{0}$

Lesson #12

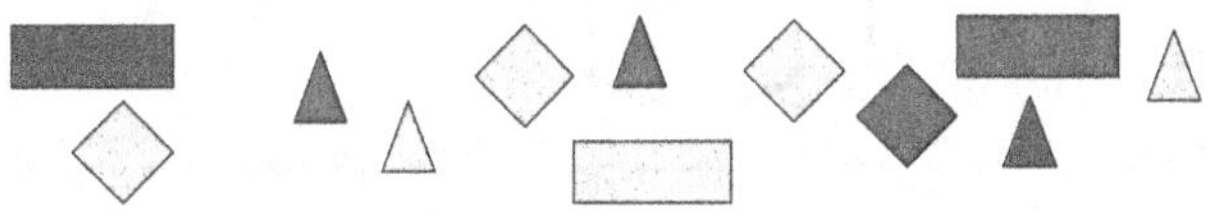

1.

2.

3.

$10 = \underline{3} + \underline{7}$

4.

5 – 6.

_4_ red   _2_ purple   _6_ yellow

Lesson #13	Lesson #14
1. 10 20 _30_ 40 50 60 _70_ 80 90 _100_	**1.**
2. _4_ + _1_ = _5_	**2.** (18) 20
3. 1 + 1 = _2_ 2 + 3 = _5_ 0 + 2 = _2_ 1 + 0 = _1_	**3 − 4.** ○○○○○○○○ ○○○○○○○○ 8 = _5_ + _3_ 8 = _2_ + _6_ ○○○○○○○○ ○○○○○○○○ 8 = _4_ + _4_ 8 = _7_ + _1_
4. 	
5 	**5.**
6. 88 _89_ _90_ 91 _92_ 93	**6.**

Lesson #15	Lesson #16
1. 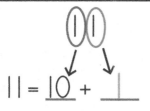 $11 = \underline{10} + \underline{1}$	1 – 2. 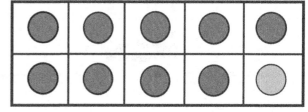 $10 = 9 + \boxed{1}$
2. 	
3. 	3 – 4.  $\underline{5}$ red $\underline{7}$ yellow
4. $0 + 0 = \underline{0}$ $2 + 1 = \underline{3}$ $5 - 1 = \underline{4}$ $4 - 3 = \underline{1}$	
5. 	5. 10 $\boxed{9}$
6. $\underline{5} + \underline{3} = \underline{8}$	6.

Lesson #17	Lesson #18
1.	1. $5 - 2 = \underline{3}$ $3 - 1 = \underline{2}$ $3 - 0 = \underline{3}$ $5 - 5 = \underline{0}$
2.	2.
3. $20 \; \underline{21} \; 22 \; \underline{23} \; 24 \; \underline{25}$	3. $40 \; \underline{50} \; 60 \; \underline{70} \; 80 \; \underline{90} \; 100$
4. $\underline{5} - \underline{3} = \underline{2}$ birds	4. $2 + 1 = \underline{3}$
5 – 6. ♡♡♡♡♡♡♥♥♥♥ ♡♡♡♡♡♥♥♥♥♥ $10 = \underline{6} + \underline{4}$ $10 = \underline{5} + \underline{5}$ ♡♡♡♥♥♥♥♥♥♥ ♡♡♡♡♡♡♡♡♥♥ $10 = \underline{3} + \underline{7}$ $10 = \underline{8} + \underline{2}$	5.
	6.

Lesson #19	Lesson #20

Lesson #19

1.

2.

3 – 4.

____ ten(s) ____ one(s) ____ 🐝 bees

(1) (9) (19)

5.

$10 = \underline{8} + \underline{2}$

6.

Lesson #20

1.

$\underline{5} + \underline{2} = \underline{7}$

2.

9 (8) (8)

3.

$5 = \underline{3} + \underline{2}$ $5 = \underline{4} + \underline{1}$

4.

$1 + 2 = \underline{3}$ $4 + 0 = \underline{4}$

$0 + 3 = \underline{3}$ $4 + 1 = \underline{5}$

5 – 6.

$\underline{3}$ △ triangles $\underline{4}$ ○ circles $\underline{6}$ ▭ rectangles

Lesson #21	Lesson #22

Lesson #21

1.

46 47 48 49 50 51

2.

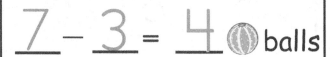

$\underline{7} - \underline{3} = \underline{4}$ balls

3.

4.

5 – 6.

 20

Lesson #22

1 – 2.

3.

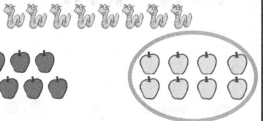

4.

$14 = \underline{10} + \underline{4}$

5.

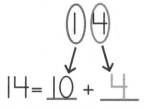

6.

$8 - 4 = \underline{4}$

Lesson #23	Lesson #24
1. $0 + 4 = \underline{4}$ $3 + 2 = \underline{5}$ $5 - 3 = \underline{2}$ $2 - 0 = \underline{2}$	**1.** $\underline{6} + \underline{2} = \underline{8}$ insects
2. $10 = \underline{5} + \underline{5}$	**2.** 9 ⑤
3. $\underline{7}$ yellow $\underline{9}$ (green)	**3.**
4. 	**4.** ② 0
5 – 6. $6 = \underline{2} + \underline{4}$ $6 = \underline{3} + \underline{3}$ $6 = \underline{6} + \underline{0}$ $6 = \underline{5} + \underline{1}$	**5.**
	6. $10 \quad 20 \quad \underline{30} \quad \underline{40} \quad 50 \quad \underline{60} \quad \underline{70}$

Lesson #25	**Lesson #26**
1. $\underline{6}$ + $\underline{4}$ = $\underline{10}$ animals	1. $1 - 1 = \underline{0}$ $5 - 1 = \underline{4}$ $3 - 2 = \underline{1}$ $4 - 2 = \underline{2}$
2 – 3. 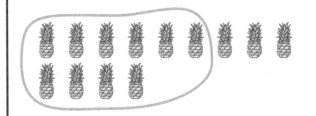 $\underline{1}$ ten(s) $\underline{3}$ one(s) $\underline{13}$ pineapples	2 – 3. 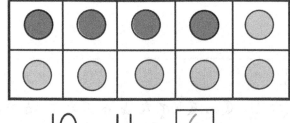 $10 = 4 + \boxed{6}$
4. (square with diagonal) ▲ ● (circled square)	4. (circled baskets)
5. 69 $\underline{70}$ 71 $\underline{72}$ 73 $\underline{74}$	5. (circled triangle) ▯ (circled △) (circled quadrilateral) ○
6. ○ ▲ (cylinder) ▯ (sphere) △ (cube)	6. $9 - 4 = \underline{5}$

Lesson #27	Lesson #28
1.	1. 60 _70_ _80_ _90_ 100
2.	2. 13
3 – 4. 9 = _6_ + _3_　　9 = _2_ + _7_ 9 = _8_ + _1_　　9 = _4_ + _5_	3. _7_ – _5_ = _2_ slices
	4. ① 5
5 – 6. _3_ △triangles　_4_ ○circles　_6_ ▯rectangles	5.
	6. ①⑦ 17 = _10_ + _7_

Lesson #29	**Lesson #30**

Lesson #29

1 – 2.

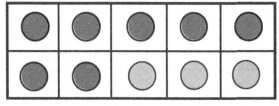

$10 = 7 + \boxed{3}$

3.

$4 + 0 = \underline{4}$ $1 + 3 = \underline{4}$

$3 + 2 = \underline{5}$ $2 + 2 = \underline{4}$

4.

5.

6.

Lesson #30

1.

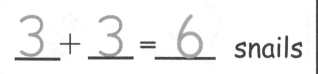 snails

$\underline{3} + \underline{3} = \underline{6}$ snails

2.

3.

4.

$10 = \underline{9} + \underline{1}$ $10 = \underline{2} + \underline{8}$

5 – 6.

$\underline{1}$ ten(s) $\underline{8}$ one(s) $\underline{18}$ dinosaurs